What Duets Can I P
Clarinet

International MUSIC Publications

Series Editors: Miranda Steel and Sadie Cook

Music arranged and processed by
Barnes Music Engraving Ltd
East Sussex TN22 4HA, England

Cover design by Headline Publicity

Published 2000

Introduction

In this *What Duets Can I Play?* collection you'll find seventeen clarinet duets that are both challenging and entertaining.

Ensemble playing is an important and enjoyable part of the learning process. These pieces have been carefully selected and arranged to create ideal supplementary material for young clarinettists who are either working towards or have recently taken an easy or intermediate clarinet examination.

Both parts of each duet are of a similar standard, and are designed so that the pupil can successfully play them with a friend or teacher. However, technical demands increase progressively throughout the book, and new concepts are gradually introduced. Each piece offers suggestions and guidelines on breathing, dynamics and tempo, together with technical tips and performance notes.

Whether it's for light relief from examination preparation, to reinforce the understanding of new concepts, or to provide useful ensemble practice, this collection will enthuse and encourage all young clarinet players.

Gymnopedie No 1

Music by Eric Satie

This was one of a set of three 'Gymnopedies' for piano. They were among Satie's earliest compositions, and were supposed to suggest a sort of purity by their simplicity and original harmonies. Satie's music was intentionally unassuming. He took this to extremes later when he wrote 'furniture music' (for an art exhibition) which was intended to be ignored.

The bottom part needs to support the top with a strong first note in each bar to create a waltz feel. As you are playing this piece, think about the fact that it was traditionally written for piano and bring out the dynamics.

Blue Danube

Music by J Strauss

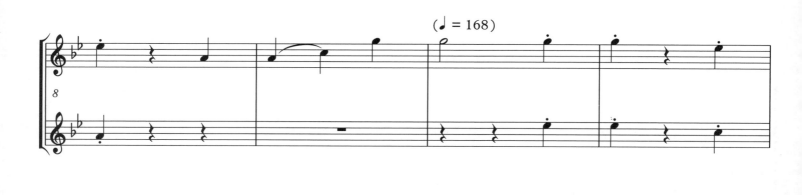

Johann Strauss the younger is perhaps best known for waltzes of such distinction that they are considered to be as much at home in the concert hall as the dance floor. However he also wrote other dances, a ballet and sixteen operettas, including *Die Fledermaus*, which translates as 'The Bat'.

This is one of his most famous waltzes. Place a slight emphasis on the first beat of each bar to lighten the overall mood. The top part will dictate the pace of the acceleration in the first section, so the bottom part needs to listen and be on the ball! And the long B flat fingering will be of use when playing the top part in bar 28.

Cavatina

Music by Stanley Myers

A *cavatina* is a short simple song or similar style of instrumental music. It is usually slow and emotional. This piece was the main theme for the five times Oscar-winning film, *The Deer Hunter*, and was a UK chart success for the classical guitarist John Williams.

This piece needs to be played expressively. The repeated quavers in the bottom part should not sound rushed, they should be relaxed in style, even when playing over the break. Take note of the dynamics. And holding the right hand fingers down between bars 17 and 19 will help the bottom part become smooth.

Stranger on the shore

Music by Acker Bilk

This piece was a remarkable hit for Acker Bilk in 1962 when it topped the charts in both the UK and the US. In the UK it was in the best-sellers list for 55 weeks! Acker Bilk's real name is Bernard Stanley Bilk, but he was given the nickname 'Acker' which is a Somerset term that means 'friend' or 'mate'.

A classic piece of clarinet repertoire – let yourself go here! A strong sound will be enhanced by thinking about producing a steady stream of air that travels all the way from the diaphragm, through the clarinet, and to the back of the room you are playing in!

Greensleeves

Music traditional

This is a traditional English tune which was well known in Shakespeare's time. Shakespeare refers to it twice in *The Merry Wives of Windsor*. The first known reference to it is in a work written in 1580, where it is called 'a new Northern Dittye'. In the twentieth century, Ralph Vaughan Williams elaborates on it in 'Fantasia on Greensleeves'.

This piece needs to be played with lots of expression. Play through the phrases, always thinking towards the last note in the phrase rather than the next note you are going to play.

14

You needed me

Words and Music by Randy Goodrum

'You Needed Me' originally had chart success with Canadian-born singer Anne Murray, winning her a Grammy Award in 1978. More recently, it has been released by Boyzone, getting to number one in the UK charts.

A good performance of this piece will be made if you play with lots of expression. Try and make your playing as smooth as possible. There are some huge intervals, which will need practice. Adding the dynamics will help produce the desired effect.

Blue moon

Music by Richard Rodgers

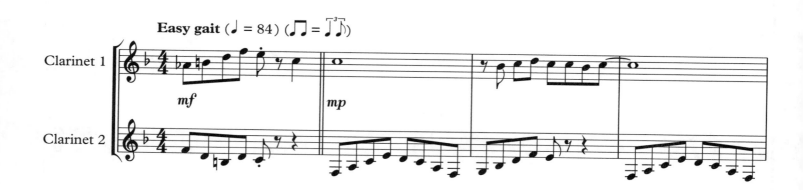

Richard Rodgers' collaboration with the lyric writer of this song, Lorenz Hart, was prolific and successful, lasting more than twenty years. Despite the seamlessness of their work, they were very different characters. Hart was undisciplined and worked haphazardly, scribbling things down on scraps of paper which he sometimes lost, while Rodgers was the opposite, working methodically to a daily routine.

Lots of scale practice is good preparation for this piece. Keep the quavers even in the bottom part, and listen carefully to the melody in order to give the piece a laid back feel.

I got you babe

Words and Music by Sonny Bono

Sonny Bono was married to Cher when he wrote this song, and they performed it as a duet. (Cher may have felt that her real name, Cherilyn Sarkarsian La Pier, wasn't catchy enough!) However, singing was not her first love. She began working as a session singer in an attempt to finance an acting career.

This needs to be extremely rhythmical. The repeated quavers in the bottom part should provide an even pulse, with the emphasis taken away from the second quaver in each set of three. The melody is much more smooth, listen to the quavers to help with the trickier rhythms. Watch out for the key change.

Summer nights

Words and Music by Jim Jacobs and Warren Casey

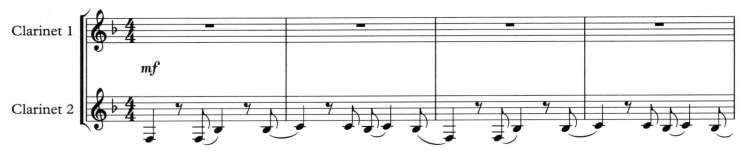

This is a song from the musical *Grease*, and in the film it was sung by John Travolta and Olivia Newton-John. It was a successful Broadway show before it was made into a film. Henry Winkler, who was playing Fonzie in *Happy Days*, was originally supposed to play the John Travolta part, but turned it down for fear of being typecast.

There is lots to think about in this piece – articulation, dynamics, rhythms and tempo changes. And getting the two parts to sound together! But you'll know the tune, and it's lots of fun to play.

I'll be there for you
(Theme from 'Friends')

Words and Music by David Crane, Marta Kauffman, Phil Solem, Danny Wilde and Allee Willis

This is the title song of the American TV show 'Friends'. It was a hit for the The Rembrandts and appears on their album *LP*. 'Friends' was not the only name that was considered for the show. 'Friends Like Us', 'Six of Us' and 'Across The Hall' were also in the running.

You'll probably know this song, but make sure you count the syncopated rhythms carefully. Practise the top part of the introduction slowly, and don't add the grace note until the rest of the section is smooth.

Music to watch girls by

Words and Music by Anthony Verona and Sid Ramin

First made popular by Andy Williams in the '60s, 'Music To Watch Girls By' was revived more recently for a car advertisement on television. In 1945 Williams dubbed Lauren Becall's singing voice in her first film with Humphrey Bogart, *To Have And Have Not*.

This must be light and energetic. Making the most of the dynamic and articulation markings will help, as will the fork key in bars 14–15 of the top part and bar 31 of the bottom part.

A string of pearls

Music by Jerry Gray

Arranger, bandleader, violinist and composer Jerry Gray had the unusual talent, even among professional musicians, of being a jazz accordionist. But he is best known for his work as a full-time arranger with the Glenn Miller band. He wrote several hits for the band, including 'String of Pearls' and 'Pennsylvania 6–5000'.

If you like jazz, you will have lots of fun playing this. The art to a good performance of this duet is getting the two parts sounding together and very rhythmical. And the last section of the top part will come with slow practice.

My heart will go on
(Love theme from 'Titanic')

Music by James Horner

'My Heart Will Go On' is the title song of the film *Titanic*. Before the film came out, much was made of the fact that it cost so much to make, and therefore stood what was thought to be a good chance of making a ruinous loss. But it was an immediate success, and Celine Dion's recording of the song is one of her best known.

This piece should be played smoothly, making the most of the dynamics. The top part reaches quite high in the clarinet register. To play it smoothly will require lots of support from the diaphragm. The bottom part contains a few tricky rhythms, so count carefully.

Coronation Street

Music by Eric Spear

Coronation Street was first shown at 7pm on the 9th of December 1960 and is the longest running TV show in the United Kingdom. A number of famous names have cropped up on the programme, including Joan Collins, Davy Jones (later of The Monkees) and Martin Shaw (Doyle from *The Professionals*).

There are a few tricky rhythms in this piece, which will be aided by your knowledge of this tune. Watch out for the accidentals and dynamics – there are lots of them!

I got rhythm

Music and Lyrics by George Gershwin and Ira Gershwin

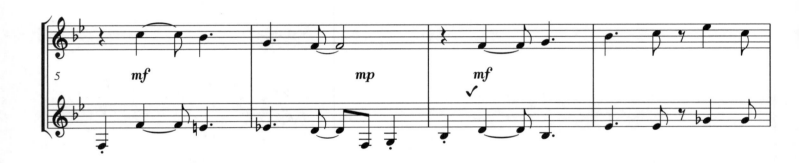

Brothers George and Ira Gershwin achieved popular and lasting critical success writing songs for stage musicals. George wrote the music and Ira the words, though George was younger and only took up the piano when the family brought one for his older brother. 'I Got Rhythm' is from the Broadway show *Girl Crazy*.

As the title suggests, rhythm has a particularly important part to play in this piece! Paying special attention to the articulation will give your playing the desired effect, as will emphasising the dynamics.

The X-files

By Mark Snow

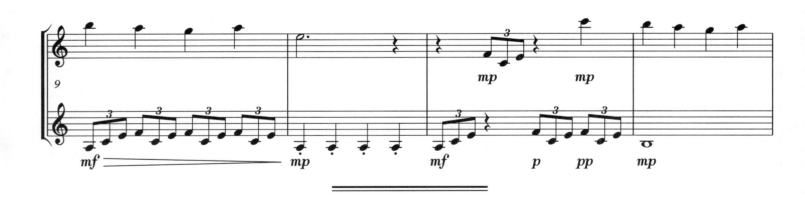

This is the title music to the American television programme of the same name. Composer Mark Snow also wrote the music for the film spin-off. The working title of the film was Blackwood, named after an Englishman, Algernon Blackwood, who wrote about a race of intelligent beings who predated humans.

This piece requires teamwork! Where the triplet sections are shared between the two parts, you will need to practise slowly, in order to incorporate the dynamics. Prepare for the high C, which starts the phrase on bar 8 in the top part, by taking a good breath in advance.

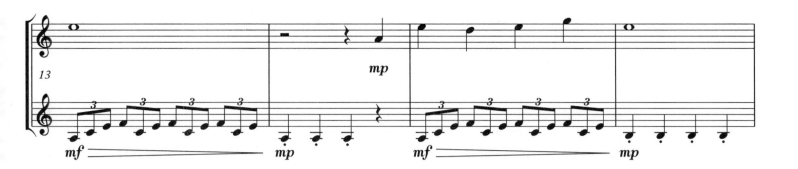

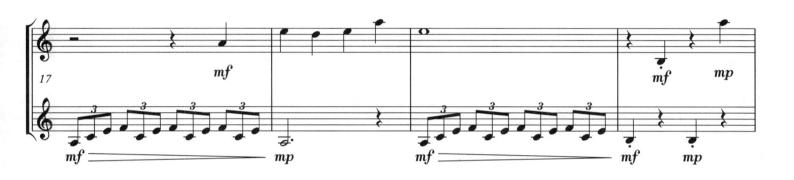

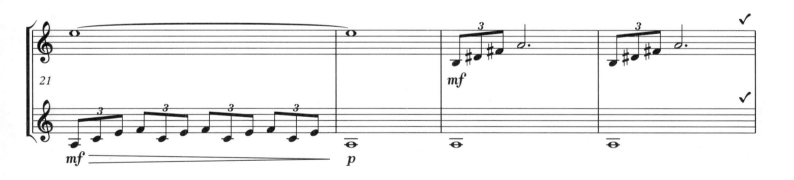

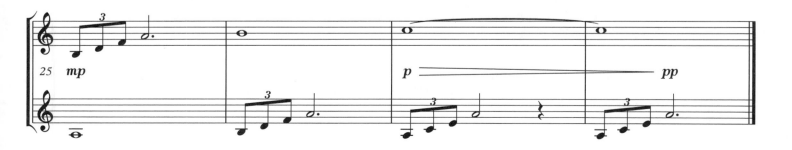

American patrol

Music by F W Meacham

Most famously recorded by Glenn Miller, 'American Patrol' became one of his hits that is instantly recognisable even now. He released it in 1942, and in the same year enlisted into the US army. He was too old to fight, but was made a captain and sent to Europe to entertain the Allied troops.

Don't worry – this isn't as tricky as it looks! Once you have mastered the rhythms, concentrate on getting the two parts to sound together, sounding as 'military band-ish' as possible. Finally, see if you can add the grace notes, without losing the rhythmical quality of this march.

Why not extend your repertoire with:

Congratulations!
You've Just Passed Grade 1

6796A
**Alto
Saxophone**

6797A
Clarinet

6794A
Flute

6798A
Piano

6795A
Violin

- Features standard repertoire which is ideal for Grades 1-2.
- Available for clarinet, alto saxophone, flute and violin with piano accompaniment; and piano solo.
- A wide variety of titles from jazz to pop, and from classical to folk.
- Fifteen great progressive titles in each book.

Series includes: *Angels – Autumn Leaves – Blueberry Hill – Bye Bye Blackbird – Don't Bring Lu Lu – The Hippopotamus Song – How Do I Live – I Don't Want To Miss A Thing – I'm Forever Blowing Bubbles – I've Got No Strings – Jeepers Creepers – My Heart Will Go On*

International
MUSIC
Publications

Available from all good music shops

You can be the featured soloist with
TAKE THE LEAD

Collect these titles, each with demonstration and full backing tracks on CD.

90s Hits	Movie Hits	TV Themes	Christmas Songs	The Blues Brothers
e Air That I Breathe (mply Red)	Because You Loved Me (Up Close And Personal)	Coronation Street	The Christmas Song (Chestnuts Roasting On An Open Fire)	She Caught The Katy And Left Me A Mule To Ride
ngels (obbie Williams)	Blue Monday (The Wedding Singer)	I'll Be There For You (theme from *Friends*)	Frosty The Snowman	Gimme Some Lovin'
ow Do I Live (eAnn Rimes)	(Everything I Do) I Do It For You (Robin Hood: Prince Of Thieves)	Match Of The Day	Have Yourself A Merry Little Christmas	Shake A Tail Feather
Don't Want To Miss A Thing (erosmith)	I Don't Want To Miss A Thing (Armageddon)	(Meet) The Flintstones	Little Donkey	Everybody Needs Somebody To Love
l Be There For You (he Rembrandts)	I Will Always Love You (The Bodyguard)	Men Behaving Badly	Rudolph The Red-Nosed Reindeer	The Old Landmark
y Heart Will Go On (eline Dion)	Star Wars (Main Title) (Star Wars)	Peak Practice	Santa Claus Is Comin' To Town	Think
omething About The Way ou Look Tonight (lton John)	The Wind Beneath My Wings (Beaches)	The Simpsons	Sleigh Ride	Minnie The Moocher
ozen (adonna)	You Can Leave Your Hat On (The Full Monty)	The X-Files	Winter Wonderland	Sweet Home Chicago
rder ref: 6725A – Flute	Order ref: 6908A – Flute	Order ref: 7003A – Flute	Order ref: 7022A – Flute	Order ref: 7079A - Flute
rder ref: 6726A – Clarinet	Order ref: 6909A – Clarinet	Order ref: 7004A – Clarinet	Order ref: 7023A – Clarinet	Order ref: 7080A - Clarinet
rder ref: 6727A – Alto Saxophone	Order ref: 6910A – Alto Saxophone	Order ref: 7005A – Alto Saxophone	Order ref: 7024A – Alto Saxophone	Order ref: 7081A - Alto Saxophone
rder ref: 6728A – Violin	Order ref: 6911A –Tenor Saxophone	Order ref: 7006A – Violin	Order ref: 7025A – Violin	Order ref: 7082A - Tenor Saxophone
	Order ref: 6912A – Violin		Order ref: 7026A – Piano	Order ref: 7083A – Trumpet
			Order ref: 7027A – Drums	Order ref: 7084A - Violin